Welcome to an underwater world!

This is Molly the mermaid.

These are her friends,

Marina,

Coral...

...and Oliver the octopus.

Look out for Walter the seahorse too. You'll find him in every picture.

Solve the puzzles in this book and help Molly and her friends put on an underwater concert.

Molly loves to sing. When she sits on the rocks and sings, all the sea creatures come out to listen.

4

Can you find two fish that look exactly the same?

Can you spot these things?

three seagulls

a lighthouse

a seal

5

Marina and Coral love to dance. They're always practising their dance routines.

Can you spot these things?

two shells

a lobster

a pearl necklace

6

The dolphins are joining in.
Which one can't quite keep up?

Molly and her friends are exploring an old shipwreck. Coral discovers two oil drums.

Can you spot these things?

a message in a bottle

a spoon

three pink plants

8

Can you help the others get to her?

9

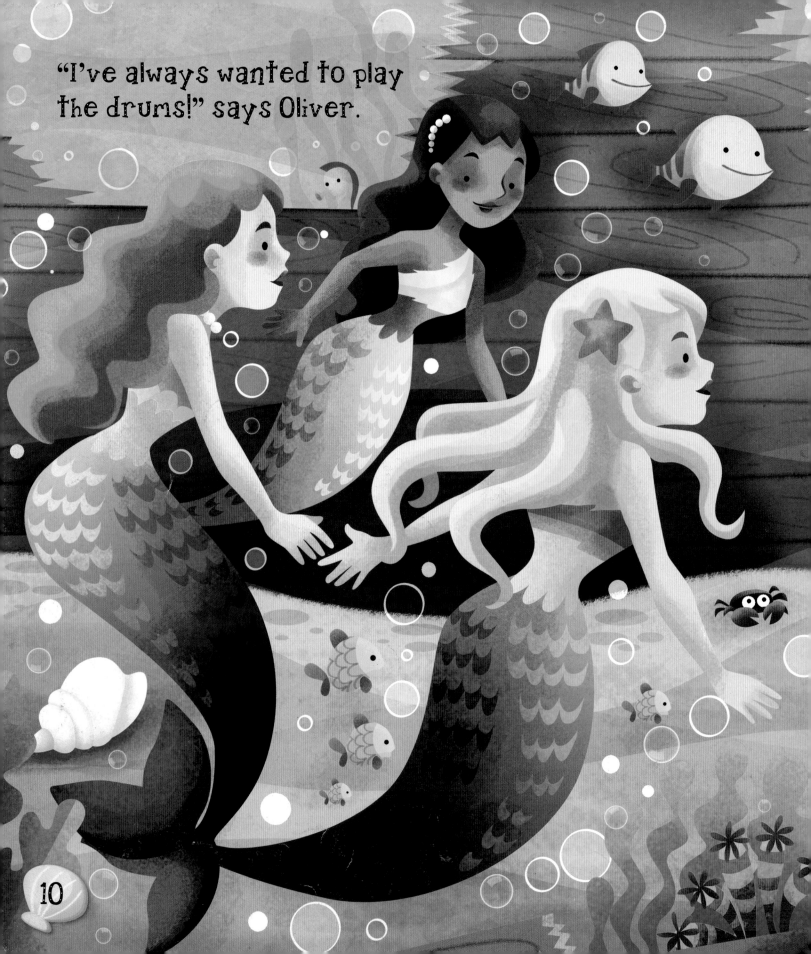

"I've always wanted to play the drums!" says Oliver.

10

Oliver's drums look almost the same, but can you find three differences between them?

Can you spot these things?

a big white shell

a crab

a lantern

11

Then Molly has an idea. "Let's put on a concert!"
she says. "We can make our own instruments
from things that we find."

12

Follow the seaweed and see what everyone finds.

Can you spot these things?

an eel

three
yellow fish

two red flowers

13

Molly makes a poster to tell everyone about the show.

THE SPARKLE SCALES in CONCERT

Saturday Night

BRING YOUR FRIENDS!

Molly has used every coloured pencil in her set – except one. Which colour hasn't she used?

Can you spot these things?

a ruler

a pair of scissors

two starfish

Marina and Coral make necklaces and bracelets for everyone to wear.

Can you spot these things?

a black and white fish

two turtles

two pink flowers

16

Can you find a
matching bracelet
for each necklace?

17

The band practise every day in a secret underwater cave.

18

Can you help Molly find the others?

Can you spot these things?

two green fish

a stingray

a sun made of pebbles

19

On the day of the concert, the audience start to arrive. Everyone's there – even the shark family!

Can you spot these things?

Molly's cousin

a handbag

Oliver's sister

20

Can you find all four members of the shark family?

21

Then a chariot pulled by two dolphins appears. Everyone gasps. It's Neptune, the King of the Sea!

The dolphins look almost the same, but can you spot four differences between them?

Can you spot these things?

two seahorses

two orange fish

a treasure chest

23

Molly and her friends begin to play. Everyone loves the music – especially King Neptune!

Can you spot these things?

a red eel

a pink hairband

a dancing turtle

24

Oliver is wearing his favourite stripy bandana. Can you see three more yellow and white stripy things in the picture?

25

"That was wonderful!" says King Neptune after the concert. "I haven't had so much fun in years!"

26

The king gives them thank-you presents from his treasure chest. Can you lead each of the friends to the right present?

Can you spot these things?

three jelly fish

a baby whale

two gold coins

27

Answers

The two fish that look exactly the same are circled in red.

The dolphin that can't quite keep up is circled in red.

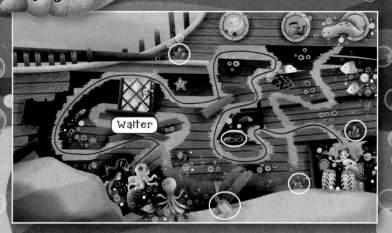

Follow the red line to get to Coral and the oil drums.

The three differences are circled in red.

Pages 12-13

Follow the colourful lines to find out what each mermaid finds.

Pages 14-15

The orange pencil is the only one that hasn't been used on the poster.

Pages 16-17

Follow the red lines to match the bracelets to the necklaces.

Pages 18-19

Follow the red line to the others.

Answers

Pages 20-21

The four members of the shark family are circled in red.

Pages 22-23

The four differences between the dolphins are circled in red.

Pages 24-25

Pages 26-27

Walter

Walter

The other yellow and white stripy objects are circled in red.

Follow the coloured lines to lead each of the four friends to their present!

31

More mermaid fun

Mermaid day!

Dress up as a mermaid for the day! Wear a coloured vest-top or swimsuit and a sarong or a large colourful scarf to wrap around your waist to make a tight, ankle length skirt, like a tail. Ask your friends to dress up too. You could even have a mermaid-themed party!

Make a mermaid picture game

Take two sheets of blue or green paper. Ask an adult to cut short rows of wavy slits across one of the sheets, without cutting the edges of the paper. Glue all around the edges, and stick the second sheet on top. Draw and cut out mermaids and push them into the slits so they seem to be coming out of the sea.

Make your own instruments

Make maracas by wrapping masking tape or gluing strips of plain paper around two plastic bottles. Then paint them. Half-fill the bottles with dried beans and shut them firmly. Then play some music, dance and shake your maracas!

Make a pretty necklace

If you don't have seashells use pasta instead! Find some pasta tubes and paint them different colours with poster paints. When they're dry, thread them onto wool or string to make necklaces and bracelets.